Repertoire

Flute

The fun way to learn!

Sarah Watts

kevin mayhew

kevin mayhew

First published in Great Britain in 2004 by Kevin Mayhew Ltd
Buxhall, Stowmarket, Suffolk IP14 3BW
Tel: +44 (0) 1449 737978 Fax: +44 (0) 1449 737834
E-mail: info@kevinmayhewltd.com

www.kevinmayhew.com

This edition © Copyright 2004 Kevin Mayhew Ltd.

The music in this book is protected by copyright and may not be reproduced
in any way for sale or private use without the consent of the copyright owner.

ISBN 978 1 84417 225 2
ISMN M 57024 311 2
Catalogue No. 3611814

Cover design: Rob Mortonson
Music setting: Donald Thomson

Printed and bound in Great Britain

Contents

	Score	Part	*CD Track
Café du Festival	12	4	5 (15)
Gobstoppers and grandads	20	8	9 (19)
Goings on	4	2	1 (11)
In cognito	22	9	10 (20)
Lavender blue	8	3	3 (13)
One for me	14	5	6 (16)
Secret Saz	10	4	4 (14)
Straight and narrow	6	2	2 (12)
The boccy chiccy!	16	6	7 (17)
When Paddy met Bella	18	7	8 (18)

Numbers in brackets are for the backing track

GOINGS ON

© Copyright 2004 Kevin Mayhew Ltd.
It is illegal to photocopy music.

STRAIGHT AND NARROW

For Betty Watts
LAVENDER BLUE

SECRET SAZ

CAFÉ DU FESTIVAL

With a little panache (𝅗𝅥. = 46) (one in a bar feel)

Repertoire

Sarah Watts

GOINGS ON

STRAIGHT AND NARROW

© Copyright 2004 Kevin Mayhew Ltd.
It is illegal to photocopy music.

For Betty Watts
LAVENDER BLUE

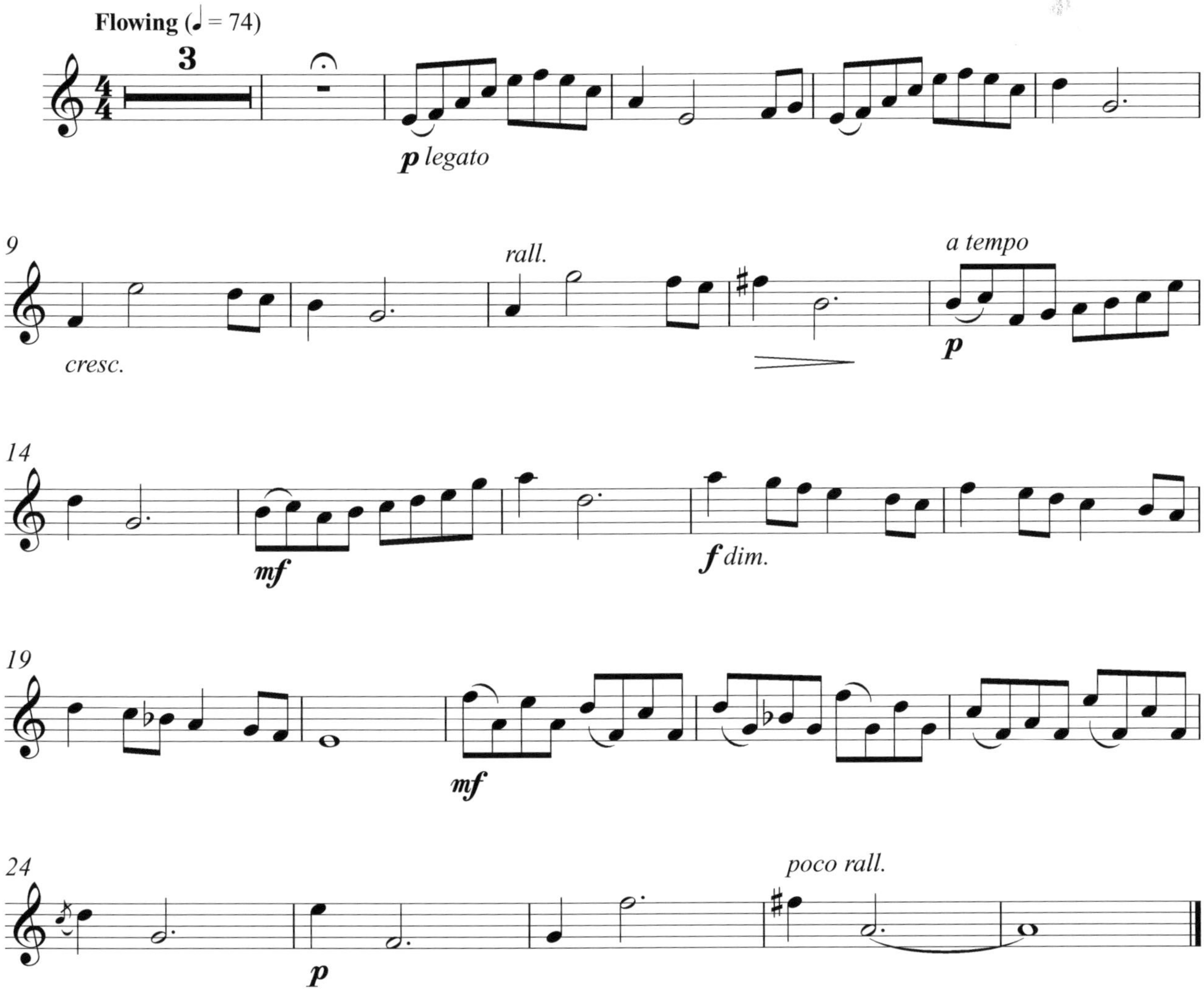

SECRET SAZ

With movement (♩ = 120)

CAFÉ DU FESTIVAL

With a little panache (𝅗𝅥. = 46) **(one in a bar feel)**

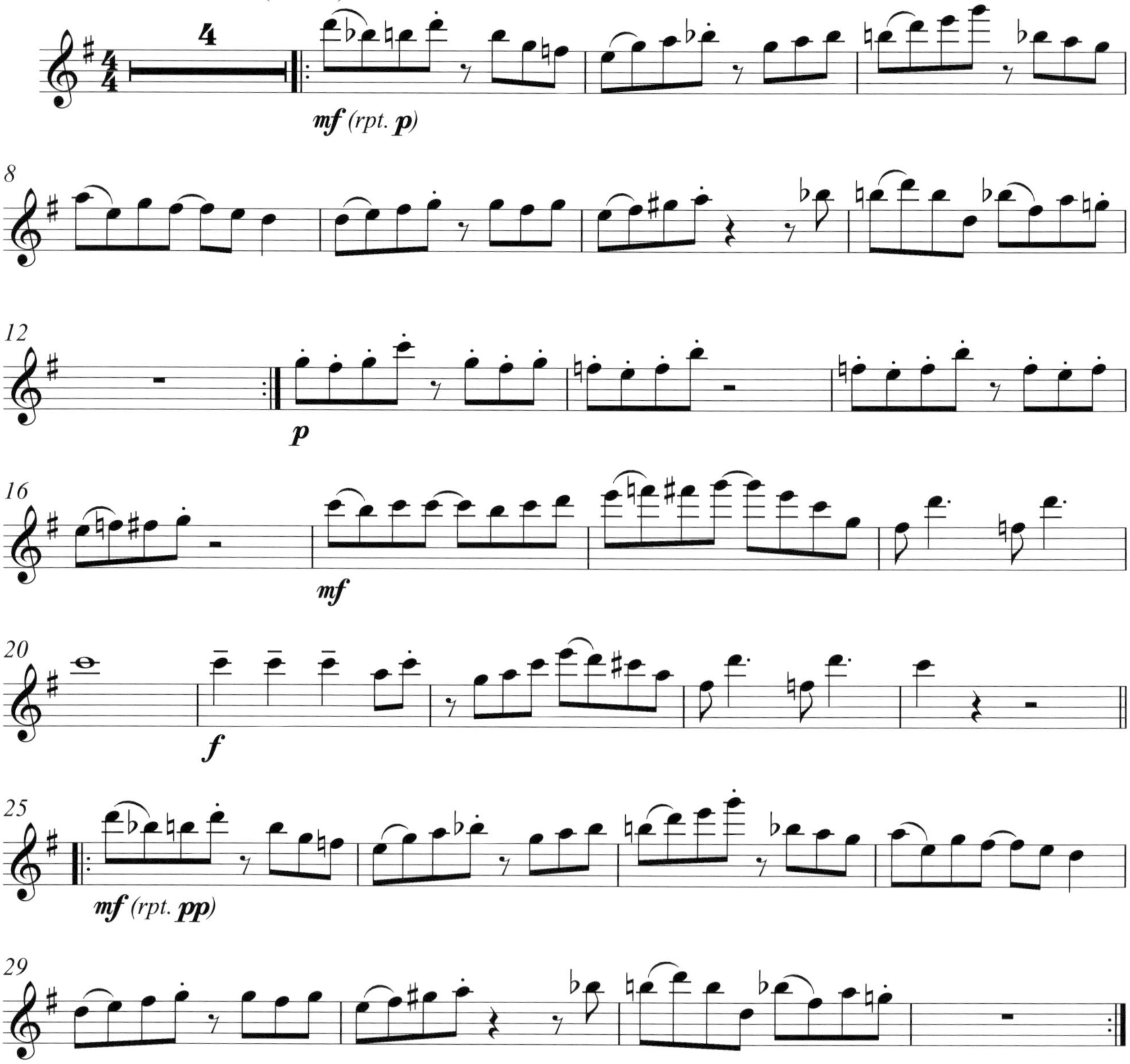

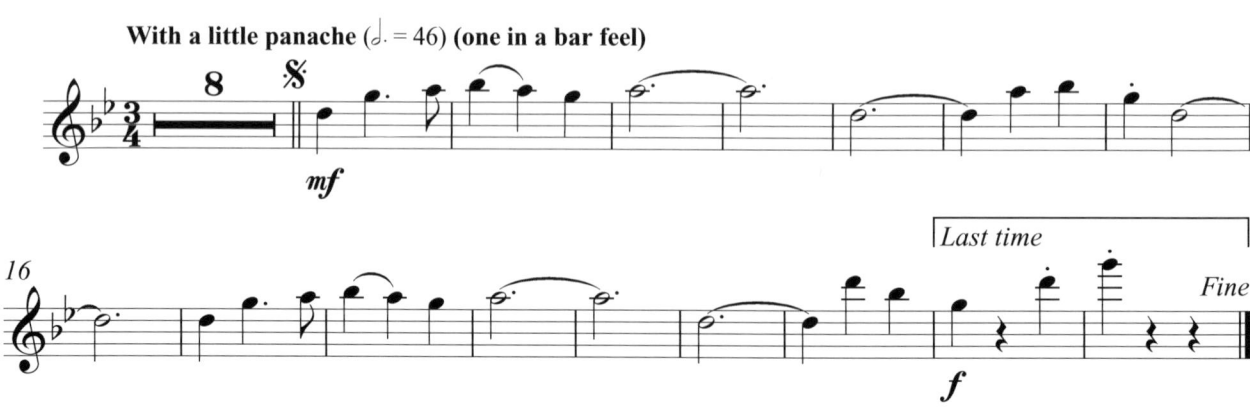

ONE FOR ME

THE BOCCY CHICCY!

WHEN PADDY MET BELLA

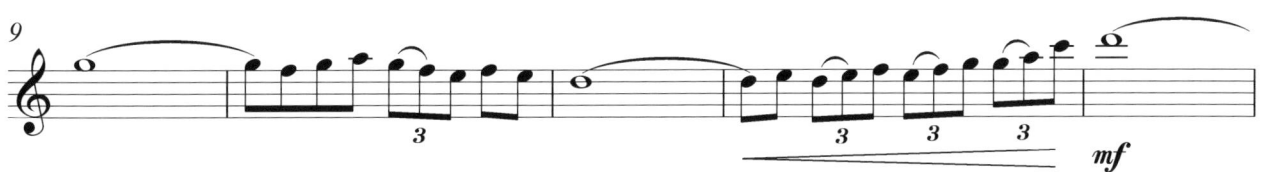

For Alex Bradley

GOBSTOPPERS AND GRANDADS

IN COGNITO

Kevin Mayhew Ltd, Buxhall, Stowmarket, Suffolk, IP14 3BW, UK
Tel: +44 (0) 1449 737978 Fax: +44 (0) 1449 737834
www.kevinmayhew.com

ONE FOR ME

THE BOCCY CHICCY!

WHEN PADDY MET BELLA

for Alex Bradley
GOBSTOPPERS AND GRANDADS

© Copyright 2004 Kevin Mayhew Ltd.
It is illegal to photocopy music.

IN COGNITO

© Copyright 2004 Kevin Mayhew Ltd.
It is illegal to photocopy music.